YMINLA?

YMINLA?

An Angeleno Explains Life on the Left Coast to His Mother in Brooklyn

DANIEL NUSSBAUM

HarperSanFrancisco
An Imprint of HarperCollins*Publishers*

For Anna and Alice

Four of these stories have been previously published: UWANNA KNOW YMINLA? in *The New York Times Magazine,* an earlier version of 2MOROWS KARS COME2LA in *I.D.*; SILENT SPRINGE in *Sierra,* and DICKENZ AA XMAS KAROLLE in *The San Jose Mercury News.*

A TREE CLAUSE BOOK HarperSanFrancisco and the author, in association with the Basic Foundation, a not-for-profit organization whose primary mission is reforestation, will facilitate the planting of two trees for every one tree used in the manufacture of this book.

e-mail address: nuss@earthlink.net

HarperCollins Web Site: http://www.harpercollins.com

HarperCollins®, ®, HarperSanFrancisco™, and A Tree Clause Book® are registered trademarks of HarperCollins Publishers Inc.

FIRST EDITION

Library of Congress Cataloging-in-Publication Data:
Nussbaum, Daniel.
  Yminla? : an angeleno explains life on the left coast to his mother in Brooklyn / Daniel Nussbaum.—1st ed.
  ISBN 0-06-258611-4 (pbk.)
  1. American wit and humor. 2. Automobile license plates—California—Humor. 3. Automobile license plates—New York—Humor.
  I. Title.
PN6162.N88   1996
818'.5402-dc20   95-51768

96 97 98 99 00 ❖ HAD 10 9 8 7 6 5 4 3 2 1

CONTENTS

ONE: FROMNY 2LA

TWO: DAILY THOTS FER PEEPLE WHOOO DRIVIN ELLAYE

THREEE: MONDO PL8SPK

GUARANTEE

The stories in this book have been written in PL8SPK, the language of plates. Every word or phrase in the text comes from an actual vanity plate. I never waver in my adherence to this rule. Every "IT," every "THE," every "AA" appears on a real vanity plate. I don't change or edit the plates; I use them exactly as the California Department of Motor Vehicles publishes them. Then, just to make it hard, I never use any plate twice in the same story.

HOW TO READ THIS BOOK

Warning: You are entering a world where spelling *doesn't* count. Think phonetically! NYTMAYR (nightmare), KARFONE (car phone), PORQPYN (porcupine), AMURIKN (American), HELTHEE (healthy).

You'll see words missing letters. You won't miss them: MPOSIBL, DETHWSH, TAKEOVR, GDZILA, IRPLCBL (irreplaceable).

On the other hand, some words acquire extra letters. Generally, read multiple letters as single ones: SSSSHE,

NNORMAA, DRRRIVE, BOXXX, RIIIICH. Always read AA, AAA, AAAA, etc. as the article "a," and II as "I."

Numbers are used for the way they sound: CN4MITY (conformity), VINDK8D (vindicated), 3LLLING (thrilling), 1DERRRR (wonder), IMPE2US (impetuous). This goes for Roman numerals, too: UWANTII (you want to).

Letters and numbers can double as words. YMINLA (why am I in L.A.), URZBEST (you are the best), 2BJUST (to be just).

Be confident! The more you read, the easier it gets. And if you come across a truly NDSI4BL plate, check the glossary at the end of the book for help.

FROMNY 2LA

THINGS 2DO 2DAY

NOTMANY MOONZ AGO WHENNNN MONEY SEEMD EZ2GET, AMAN DYD
THRUSST HIMCELF N2 LYFE IN MNHATTN. EACHDAY HEE FOLLOWD ZEE
SAME ROUTINE.

   B4 LEEVIN HIZ DIGS INTHE EAST 80S 2GO SELL HIYEELD JUNQUE
BONDS ON WALLLST, THECAT MADE ALIST. HE ALWAZE RITES THISS
TITLE ONTOPP:

THINGS TODO TODAI.

   HERES1 TIPIKAL LIST FRRROMM THAT PERIOD:

2

```
GO2WORK          BYRLST8          GETUGLY

BMEAN            BAGRESV          TAKEOVR

BGRIM            DOMIN8           KONTROL

BSLICK           YELL             SUSOMEi

GETEVEN          CHEAT            SSTEAL

ARGUE            CALLMOM
```

THEEZE DAYS THISGUY LIVS INA LOGCABN NEAR THA CREEK INNNN
2PANGA CANYON. HEES LOOKN 4AAA JJOB WRITING SITCOMS. WILE
HEIZ LIVNG NLA HEEE DUZZZ MAKOVER HIMSELF 2DABONE.

EVRYTHG HAZ CHANGED, XCEPT THIS: EACH MORNINN THERS STILL
AA LIZT NAMD MANYA THINGG TODODO TODAY.
THISONE IZZ FROM ZE CURRENT PHASE:

BGROOVY   DOYOGA   DONWORY   BUYCAKE   EATTOFU

BEASITV   BREATHE   CHANT   VEGOUT   BMELLO

JUSTBE   2DBEACH   KIKBAKK   ENDPAIN   GO4RIDE   BFLUFFY

THEREIS AMORAL 2D STORI. ANYONE WHOOOO HAS LEFTNY CAN BECOMME
ANEWMAN ORR ANUGAL. COME2LA ANNDD LYKE GO4IT DUUUUDE. BUT
DNT4GET DAT 1DAY JUST WHEN YOUDOO SITDOWN 2MEDIT8 AJOKER WORKN
4D MANHTTN DA COULDBE BANGIN ONTHE DOOR WITH HANCUFS YN UR SIZE.

3LILPGS

IAMM APIGG. LIFENLA 8NTEZ 4US IN DPIGG COMUNTY. THATSY
IDCIDED 2SHARE DSTORY OF MEEEE ANNDD ZEE OTHERR LTLPIGS.
IFONLY 1PIGGIE OUTDER DUZZZ BENEFIT, IWILL NOT ASK4MOR.

   ITT STARTS 1DAY WHENNNN OURMOM JUST SUDNLY SNAPPS. OVRWRKD,
IGESS. SHEGOZ, "GETOUT UKIDS. BEATIT. UCANT STAY NMY PIGGI
HOUS NOMORE."

   NOBGDL. IAJUST. SODO MIII SIBS. IFIGURE ANY NORMAL MODERN
PPIGLET KANB AA HOMONER. ANDSO WEALLGO HAUSE HUNTNG.

   PIGGY1 DUZ FIND ACHARMR: AAAA RUSTIK STRAW CABINN ONA KNOLL

NEAR THA GETTY MUSEUMM NMALIBU. "WITH AAA TRUULY 2DIE4 OCEANVU," DUH RLST8 AGENTT SAYS.

ENTER "THEWOLF": THE WYLDFYR OFD DECADE, DRIVEN WITHOUT REMORSE BIII SSPOOKY SANTAA ANA WINDS. WHOOSHH. THEY HUFNPUF ANND INONE INSTANT NOTHIN REMAINZ UV ZHOUSE CEPTIN SMOKENN ASH.

THE2ND PIGGLET FELNLUV WYTHE ANOLD CRFTMN SSTYLE FXRUPPR CLOSE TU MCARTHR PARKE. IMGOIN, "JEEPERZ CREEPRS, UDO NOTT WANT2 LIVIN THISS UNSAFE AREA."

"YESIDOO," PIGGGEE SEZ. "DOUSEE THEY MADE ZIS NCHNTNG HOUZ FROM NUTNBUT TWIGS? UCANT FINDEM THATWAY ANYMORE."

ENTRR "ZWOLF." INN THERIOT THAT FOLLOWD THE1ST RODNEEY

KINGG VERDICT, HAVOC SPREAD DAYNNYT. DA TWIGGY CHATEAU NEVER HADA CHANCE.

IWENT FORR ABRICK LVT2BVR KAPEKOD WIFFF ALOW PHIXED R8 MORGAGE ON1 DLYTFUL SHADY CULDSAC YN ENCINO. MZPIGGY LIVS ONLEE 3DOORS AWAAAAY. B4 IWOULD MOVE INNN XPERT WORKERZ DYD ANN XTENSIV SEISMIC RTROFIT.

SUMTYMZ IWONDER, IZZZ EVRY1 INNNN THISONE PIGFMLY AAAAA MARKED PIGG? IDO FACE "DAWOLF" ON JAN17TH 1994. LIKE MOST PIGGIES IAM HAPILEE MAKNZS WHEN DDA EARTH THROSE AFIT. KABOOM BOOM KABOOOM. IDREAD SUNRYZ. BUT L8R ILSEE JUSAFEW CRACKSZ. IM8IT OKAAAY!

ZE OTHERR 2PIGLTS GETSOME THERAPI 4THEE MENTAL TRAUMA THAY

NDURE. ANDNOW THOZII SSHARE ACONDO NOT2 FAR FROM MYPLACE. AND
AS4 ME, ITALK2 PIGGI GROUPZ ALLOVER RTOWNE ABOUT HOW2 GETREDI
4DABIG1.

UWANNA KNOW YMINLA?

DEARRR SONN,
  URPAPA ANDI FEEL XTRMLY DSTURBD ABOUT ALLDAT RANDOM FREEWAY
GUNPLAY ONZNEWS. DONTU BELEEV THA KWALITY UV LIFE HASBEEN
SLIPPIN SWIFTLI DWNHLL OUTDER YN LSANGLS?
  IWORRY.

                                 IMAMOM

HIMOMOO,
  NOWORYZ, OKLUV? IPH BADGUYS GOBANG, ISWERVE.
                      THESON

MIBOY,

   THERIOT BRINGS VRYSCRY IMAGES 2D TUBE. IMUPALD. IMUPSET.

   NTHE50S DADNI GOT2GO 2LA. COKTLS FOR2 AT ZEE COCONT GROVE
ONN WLSHRE BLVD. LLUVLIE! 2NITE CHARLNE HUNTRR GAULTT TOLD
OFD MOB THAT LOOTS NEARBY.

   YBE SUICYDL? COMBACK TU FLTBSH SOIAM ABLE 2SLEEP.

                                        MOTHUR

MAMERE,

   THISS BEEEG NATIONAL GUARD HUMVEE CAME2 GRAB MY PARKNG
PLACE. ABIT ANNOYNG, TRUE, BUTMAAA, ISHALL NOT ABANDON MYLA.
IMUSSAY UDNTKNO MEEEE. CNTMPL8 DIS: LOADSA INOV8IV CUISEEN
STARTS HERE. IWOULD MISSDAT. PLUS L8 ATNITE JASMINE SMELLS
3LLING 2ME.

ABOVALL IMNUTZ FORTHE XKWIS8 CLIMATE! ATOTAL BLISOUT!
                                        SONNI

BOYCHIK,
   BEIRUT HAZ NICE WEATHR ALZO. ISEE UU DIDNOT MOOVOVA THERRR.
   BYDAWAY YA PHINELI GOTSUM RAIN. THOS FLOODS LOOK GRUSOM.
NOT2 CLOSE2U, IHOPE.

                                     URMOMMA

MATER,
   DONTBSO NEGITIV TOOTTSI! MHPYNOW, MHVNFUN. LTSPRTY GIRLFRN!
   NEW TOPIC: MYY XLNTTAN. BTRYET. VISITCA. IDLUVV2 SHOWYOU MY
LAP POOL.

                                   HAPYGUY

LISTENU,
  MYYBABY DDDID MOVE2 LALALND ANNDD WENTMAD. RITENOW CONNEE
CHUNG SEZ FLAMES 8UP 342 HOUSES. LGNABCH, MMALIBU, 2PANGA,
SIERRA MADRE.
  SMUG1, WHTSNXT?

                                              MOMMS

MAMAMIA
  IDO WAKEUP ONDFLOR 2WILDD SHAKIN. IM LYKE, "NONEED2 NOKNOK,
GDZILLA. JUST CUMINN."
  FEARNOT, ISRVIVE. LUCKIME, ILOST UNO FIESTA WARE BOWL.
COUNTEM ONE. ORANJE.
  NTROPY. DISARAY. LOSS. UNOWHAT? WEARE STRONGR NOW. CONFDNT.
MORE GROWNUP. DFIANT.

MAKMYDY. IDIG RUBBLE. SOTHERE.

                                        URRJOY

MEINKID.

UBIGLUG.

D8LINE ELLAYE: ITS MMUDD SEASON.

YOUMUST HAVEA DETHWSH. SERUSLY. RN4YRLF. XKAPE. IWILL BUYA
1STKLSS TKT 4U.

LETMEE TELYA HOW DA AVGJOE DUZ PIKCHA ZAT PLACE. FILTHI,
UNCVLZD, UMONGUS, BBBAD 4RAIZN AFAMLEE, ATERROR ZONE ONACCT
OFTHE FYRES, CIVIL UNREST, MESSDUP ROADWAY SYSTEM, ETCETC,
HOME2 RUUD ANDOR BZAR LOCALS, BEGGARS, REJECTS, POLITCL
FRINGE LOONIES, DV8 TTYPES, SOME IMMORAL CELEBS AND GNGSTER

TEENS ARMED WYTHE HIPOWRD ASALT WEAPONS. PLUS 1OUTOF2 GOEZ, "SORRIE_NO SPEEK ENGLISH." REGLAR FOLKS KEEP AWAAAAY FRMLA.

                              IMURMA

MAMASAN,
   URZBEST. ATLAST IKNOW HOWCUM ILOVELA. IT DOES REMINME OF NYC.
   DNT4GET 2WRITE.

                         LADUDE

IH8LA,
OR HOW2 HANDL AA NUYORKR WHOOOO STARTS RAGGING ONN LALALND

THA NOITALL NEUYRKA SAYSS: IWOULD NEVAR LIVNLA. UCAN GROWWW OLD LOOOKN 4AAA DECENT BAGELLL.

  ANDYOU REPLY: BAGELZ! BAGLS! BAGELSZ!

  DA SUPRIOR NYER GOES: TRYTO HAVA NORMAL CVILIZD SLYTLEE ELEVATD DSCUSN IN ELLAYE. MPOSIBL! NSTED UGET THISS: "SOWUTTT DOU DRIV?" ORR THISSS: "SO WHERE DOYA WORKOUT?" ORELSE THIS: "RYTENOW MIII INRCHLD FLSGOOD, BUT MY CATS INOR KITTTEN HASA

FUNGAL NFECSHN." BREADY FORTHS KYNDA INANE TWADDEL AT
ANYTIME INNN DAT TOWN.

TO WHICH UU SAI: POOR KITTTIE.

ZE SOFZTK8 NUYAWKA SAYSS: LA LACKS AAAA CERTAIN RICHNES.
YN NEWYORK ITS NEARLEE EIGHT ATNITE. SOON ALLL OVA DAA
THEATER DISTRK CURTINS WILLBEE RISING. ILUVDEE SIGHT OF
BROADWY THENN, DAT MADMAD YELLO RIVER UV TAXI CABS.

YOUUU ANSWER: DUUDE?

DUH FOOD OBSESST NEWYKER GOEZ: THERIZ NO PIZZZZA LIK
NYPIZZA INN LSANGLS.

2THAT YOU GO: BBAGELS! BAYGULS! BAGELS!

THA TYPICAL NWYORKR SEZ: IH8LA! UDO NOT HAV SEASONS THERE.

SO UUU REACT: MAYBE. BUTIN SPTMBR DE SMOGG TURNZ BROWNE.

ROZMRYS BBBABY

WHEN IGOT MARRIED 2GUY WOODHSE, THA MINORR BRODWAY AKKTOR,
INEVER DDID NTISIP8 THAT SOMDAE THIS GUDLUKN NICEMAN WOULDBE
ANAGENT UV SATAN. NOR DIDI IMAJIN HEE WUDDEVR ARRANGE 4MEEEE
2BEAR ZE DEVILSS SPAWN.

   BUT DAT WAZ B4 OUR NU NEIBORS GOTT2 HIM. BEFORE ROMAN ANNDD
MINNY, THOS 2EVIL CLDBLDD WITCHS, MADE ADEAL. ENDLSS STARDUM
4GUY YN XCHNGE 4MYCHLD.

   THATT2 WAS BEE4 IFOUND OWT ZTRUTH DHRDWY: AA NYAKTOR WILLDO
NETHING ANYTHNG NETHNG 2GET AHEAD.

IRMEMBR THINKNG, HORROR DUZ NOT HAPPENN 2YOUNG MIDLCLS WIFES LYKE ME. DUZIT? IAMMMM INNOSNT! IAM ORIGNLI FROM OMAHAAA UKNOW!

ITSEEMZ INOCENS DSNTMTR WHENNNN EVERY DEVIL WORSHPR IN MNHATN GETZ NVOLVD INA PLOTT 2CONTRL YOU.

DETALES: INN HER KITCHN MINNY GROWS ALOTTA PCULIAR POWRFUL HERBS. 1NITE GUYDOES FEEDMEE CHOCOL8 MOUSSE LACED WITH SUM. DATZME GOING N2 AN ALTERED ST8. L8R ONN SATEN HIMCELF DUZZ MBRACME. DATSME UNDER DA FOUL CREECHR WHO DUZZZ MBODY EVRYTNG BBBBAD ND WORLD. MIII HUSBAND WATCHES. ALLL ZEE WITCHYZ DO.

NEXTDAY IAM LIKE, "IDID DFN8LY HAVE1 UNHOLY NYTMAYR. WAY2SIK!" IIII ACTUALY CANN NOT REMEMBR WHAT REALI HAPPENS.

ANDTHEN FORRR 9MOS IMSHURE DBABY ICARRY ISMINE ANND GUYS PRESHS1, NOTMINE NNN ZAT THINGS.

MNWHLE WENEVER ISEE MINNEY SHE HANDS 2MEEE AAAA GGLASS FULLOF SMELLY WHITE LIQUID. "DRINKIT 2TSIE," SSSSHE SEZ. "UWANNNA HELTHEE KIDKID, DONCHA?" MINNI LIES TTO MNIPUL8 MMMME. THEY ALLL DOO.

EVEN MYYY AVUNCLR OBGYNMD IS 1OFTHEM. IDELIVRR INNN ABSOLUT FEAR. ANDNOW HEE DDUS WANTME 2BLIEVE MYBABIE FAILED 2SURVIV. NOWAAY. IKNO THEEZE WITCHES HAV MYKIDD NEXXXT DOOR. IKAN HEAR ANNNN NFANTE CRY. IGO2C.

IPRAY NO MOTHER EVR HAS2 FACE SUCHA SHOK. THOS STRANGE

DAA CURSED WWITCH INCHARJ, RROMANN, GOES, "GODSDED! BEHOLD
DUH ONLEE BGOTT1 SONAV SAYTIN!" ANDTHEN EVREY WITCHE THERE
SEZ, "HAILE SAYTON ANDSON! HALE!"

III MARRIED ASEWER NOT AMAN. IDOIDO LOATHEU, GUI. UU ANDUR
LUDICRS PALS, THEEEEZ EVIL AMORAL CULT MEMBERS WHO DYD MESSUP
MILIFE 4ALLTYM.

YESBUT AMOM IZZA MOMMU ISA MOMMO. EVEN IF MYSON SEEMS
DIFFRNT FRRROM OTHER BOYS NNNNNN GGGIRLS, SOWHATT. ICANNNN
STILLE CHANGE DIAPERS, FEED DCHILD, COMFORT DLADD WHENEVR
IHAVE2, SING2HM, TELLHIM STORIES . . .

FREEWAY FILOSFR

COGITO

RGOSUM

AHEDOVU.

SATRDAY NYTE FEVERR

HEYTONY NICE HHAIR!

ITZTONY MANERO BOPP BOP BOPPIN DOWNN DSTREET. *(BRING UP THEBGS GOIN AHHH AH AHAH STAYING ALIVE, STAYNG AALIVE)*

TONEEE, YNGNWLD TTONY, DROOLN OVERA POLYSTR SHIRT INA STORRS WINDOWW. TONII WHOOO DUZZ LIKE2 EATPZZA ONTHE SIDEWLK, CHKNOUT THE LADEEEZ ANATOMY. TONYM, CUTEBOD, NOFUTUR.

THERZ GOT2BE 100 REASONS WHYYYY TOHNEE WILNOT EVERR XCAPE STIFLNG, REPRESD BAYRDGE, BRKLYN. MOMNDAD, HIZ FRENZ, TONYYYY

22

HIMCELF: NON CAN IMAJINN SURVIVN YN AWORLD BEYOND THA BELT PARKWAY.

BUT PUT TONY ONDA DANSE FLOORE ANDTHEN SUDNLY THERIZ NNO ROTTTEN EKONOMI, NNOE HOSTILE PARENTZ, NOOO SCAREY LOWLIFE HOMBOYZ, NO GRIM REALITI AT ALLL.

NOOOO BROOKLN. THEREIS ONLYE DISCO.

STEPONE STEPP2 STEP3. (USHUD BEDANCN YEAAA, DANCNNN YEA!) ANNDD BBACK2 THREEE. SHAKEIT NOW! SHAYK IT! REACH DOWNN. REACHUP. POSE.

OWOWMAN JJJJJOY.

TOENEEE 1DERS HOW2 NCORPR8 THISSS O2SWEET 2HAPPIE 2REAL FEELIN N2LIFE OUTZIDE THECLUB. HIZZ DDDANCE PARTNUR, STEFENI

(MORE THANA WOOMAN, MORDEN AWOMAN 2MEEEE), SEZ, "YEAHBUT TONIEEE MOVE2 MNHATTN. ITZ DFFRNT THERE, BETTAH."

SOOO RHERO DUZ SUMTHNG TRUULY CURAJUS. HEEE CROSSES DUH EAST RIVER.

HIZ AGENT SPEAKS 2GDZLLA

GODZYLA, PAL, THISIS WUT YOUDO BETTRN NE1 NFILMS: RKHAVOC.
UPLAY LARJE HARMFUL REPTILE AND YURAGOD AT IT. TRUULY. UBAD,
LIZARD, YOUBAD.

   1STTIME ISAWU WORK, STOMPIN ON TOKYO, FRYIN IT2, ISEZ,
"ILUVDIS RMRKABL VICIOUS SCALY CREECHR DAT CALLS ITSELF
GDZILAA. IWANNA HELP GDZILA HAVEA FAABULS CAREER."

   SO MISTERR MONSTAH, IBEG YA, LISSN TU YURAGNT ANNDD REPEAT
AFTRME: GDZZILLA DUZZ NOT DO MUSIKAL COMEDY. AGAIN.
GDZYLLA . . .

SSUNSET BLVD

BIGGR THANN STRSAND. EVEN BIGGRN OPRAH. IN HERTIME, THA SILENT FILMMM ERA, DA1 MOST LIKELY 2START AWILD FRENZI JUSST BYYYY SHOWNUP, ZE GR8IST STARRR WRLDWYD BARNONE WUZ NORRMA DESMOND. SOLUVED, SSO MADCAPP, SO RIIIICH: AGIANT CELEB LIKEDAT DUZ RULE THISS BURG.

   LIKE THETIME APRINCE FFFROMM BOMBAY DESIRED AA SILK STOKIN FROMHER. HE DDID BEG4ITT, OPLEEES MISS, DEN USED IT 2OFF HIMSELV. SUDNLEE TAKE AWAAAY ZAT KINDA PPOWERR ANDA PERSONN CUDD WINDUP MUCH2 WARPD.

2DAY YN 1950 NORMAA DSMOND HAS NOT STOOD NFRONT OFD KAMERA SSINCE TALKIES GOTHOTT. LIKA DEPOSED MONARK, SHEDUZ LIVE AL1 WID MAXXX. JUSTD AGING MOVIE IKON NN MAX DBUTLER INNNN HER NGLECTD JUMBEAU ROCOCO PALACIO ON SSUNSET BLVD.

ABOUT MMMMAX: NOTA TYPICAL SERVANT. OVRQLFD, 4STRTRS. IMAGYN LEONRDO ASA BAGBOY. HESTHE1 WHO DDID DSCOVER NORMA AT17. THENN WENTON 2DIRECT HIZZ PRIZE INN SOMANY 1DAFUL PHILMZ. MARRIED HERTOO, THE1ST 1OF5 HUSBNZ.

NOWWWWW MAXX DUZ WUTEVR HEHAS TODO 2PROTEC HIZ HILY EMSHNL EXWIFE FROMD BADNUUZ THAT SHEHAZ NNO CAREER: HEEE CONCOX PHONY FANMAIL DAYLIE, VACUUMS.

ADD2 THS ODDBALL HOME SCENE MRJOE GILLIS, WHOOOO ARRIVES

1DAY BYAXDNT. JOEGOES, "W8. IKNOW YU. YOU USED2 BEBIG."
MILYON DOLLR EYES ABLAZE, LA DEZMOND WILLNOT HEARIT: "IAMMMMM
BIGG! PICTURS GOT SMALLL!"

WELLLL ITSA STARRT. BFORE 2LONG JJOH LIVES INSYDE THEBIG
HAUS. SHEEEZ GOING, "IWANNA BUYSOM SUITS 4UJOE. TWENTEE!
NDULJME." 4DSTARR, HAVING THISSS YNGRMAN AROUND WORKS LYKE AN
ELIXIR. SHEEEEE WILLL PERKUPP LOTS, FILLUP DA POOL AGAIN ANND
FINALLI GETTHE OLDKAR ONDROAD.

WITHIN NORMAZ PRIVATE UNIVRS, PARAMNT STUDIO IZ ALWAYZ
ABOUT2 CALLHER. SHEHAZ JO, AAAA SCRNRTR, LOOKN OVEH THE
SCRIPT SSSSHE WROTEBY HERSELF 4HERSLF 2STARR INNN.

"ILIKEIT," JOSEZ, NOT2 SINCERE. "EXCEPTN, NE1 EVR TELYA YOU4GOT 2WRITE DIALOG?"

NNORMAA 2JOE: "WEDID NOT NEED ANYA DAT! WEEEE HD FAYCES!"

READER, IF WE STRIPP AWAAAY ALLDIS CHATTER, BASICLY WEVE GOTTA DELUZNL AGING DIVA FULLOF PSEUDO SSELF CNFDNCE HOOO DYD BUY ALOT UV LUXUREE GIFTS 4A WIZEGY SHE HARDLEE KNEW.

LETS CNTMPL8 JOEZ DOWNHIL RYDE. 1TIME HESED, "PLEEZ, LADY, AGIGOLO? THISIS NOTT MYTRIPP." NORMAZ REPLY: SSSSHE SLITS HERR WRIST.

AND JOEEE STAYZ. NNNN STAZE. UNTIL EVEN2LY, FEDUP PLUS FURIOSO ATT BEING CAGED JJOE ATTAXX NORMAAA WYTHE DATRUTH:

SHEEEZ TOOTOO OLDE 2PLAY AGIRL.

"NOTEVEN UCAN CHANGE REALITI," SAYS JOEH. "OK LFSABMR. DLWITIT. IGOTAGO."

ANDSO PLANETT DESMND GETZ KRUSHD 4GOOD. FLPTOUT ANNDD ARMED SHEDID START TU FYR. BAM! SHEGOZ,"NO1! NOTU! NOBODY CAN LEAV ASTARR!" BAMBAAM!

JOEJOE DUZZZ STAGGR BAKWRDS F8LEE WOUNDED N2DNYTE. WHENNNN NEWSREL REPORTR DUDESZ REACH THGR8 MANSHUN ONSNSET THEY OGLE THEBOD AFLOAT INDA SWMPOOL.

TWISTED NORMA THINKS THCROWD DAT TURNS UP IZZA FILMCRU. THATZIT. OLDPAL CBDMIL WANTZII SHOOT THEBIG SCENE. ATLAZZT!

HLYWOOD HAZ2BE THEMOST KRUEL PLACE ONEARTH. YOUARRE BGRNLFE ANDTHEN URAJOKE. THLGND FEELS VINDK8D, ALIVE SPEAKIN 2A FANTOMM CREW: "IMSOHPY 2BEEE BACK ONA SET! IPROMIS NEVA2 LEAVEU!" AAAAA BUNCHA FUZZZZ ANNDE MEDIA HYENA CREEPOS LOOK BAK.

ANDNOW WECANN SEEE NNORMAA GLIDING DOWNN HR GRAND CIRCLER STAIRWY. SEE OUR TRAGIC SISTERR INNNN ILLUSHN, WHOSEZ, "IMREDI 4MI CLOSEUP MR DEMILLE."

2MOROWS KARS COME2LA
AA PLAYINN 1ACT

CURTNUP ONDA CITY UV ELLAYE. SHEIS ONE 4TEEISH, XHAUSTD BUT
GUDLUKN TATOOD SNGLMOM. ATHOME. PACENG BAKN4TH. LOADZ ONN
HERMIND.

DOORBEL SOUNDS. ITS THISS HYPER LTLGUY. NAME: 2MOROWS KARS.
THEEZ TWO GGO WAYBAK.

LSANGLS: UAGAIN! YIAWTTA!

AUTOS 2B *(PUSHIN HIZWAY N2 THE LVNGRM)*: VROOOM! VRROOOM! GTREADY 4HAPPY HAPPII FUNCARS!

LLAA: OBUGOFF UWEERDO! GETTOUT! YOUME ANNDD FFFFUN DONOT EXISTO YN THA SAME UNIVERS NEMOORE.

WEEELZ 4TOMORA *(TAKIN OFFENSE)*: WHAAAA? YOUDOO LUVCARS. FUZZZIE DICE. AGIANT TAILFIN. TUKNROL UPLSTRY . . .

LOTUS LLAND: PAST TENSE. ILOVD.

NEWCARS DUUUDE: . . . PHAMOUS CARRS. REMEMBR JUNE17 1994? 1NATION SITTIN NTHRALD, ALLEYEZ WATCHIN ZEE WHITE BRONKOH, ANDYOU, ELL AAY. WTARUSH!

TNSLTWN: PLEZGOD. NOMORE OJS.

CARS 4MANANA: NONONO. NOT JUSTDAT. IMHERE TTO DCLARE ANUAGE 4DRIVIN WILLBEE HERE4U SOON. *(STARTT CHIRPYY MUSIC)* LOS ANGELES, PLEEESE JOINME ASI TAKATRP INNNN 2MOROS AWTOE.

OURTOWN: GOAWAYY! GBYE!

FUTURE CARGUY *(OBLVIUS)*: HEYLOOK! WEDONT STEER DWAY UDO. WEDRIVE NGENIUS WAY2CUL HITEK INNOV8V MACHINZ THAT RESPOND 2VOICES. "GO2 DA DRY KLEANER." "BEATDIS LITE." "FASTRR." BETRYET, UNSEEN FORCE FIELDZ MEAN WENEVER KRASHHH!

DACOAST: IM CALLING 911.

MSTRR LOOK4WD TOA NUDAY: B4U DO, WONTYA EXAMIN THEEZZ UTTERLY FASN8NG GRAFFIK DSPLAYS? LUKATME ONTHE TOTILEE AU2MATQ CMPTRZD SMART FREEWAY. ICAN SIMPLI PUNCHIN MYEXIT ANDNOW THEREIS NOTHIN 4MEEEE 2DO XCEPTN 2RELAAX. INDASH SCREENZ LETMEE KNO ITZ ALLOK. OGOODY! GOTENUF TIME 2NJOYY AROUND OF VIRTUAL GGGOLF.

SOCALIF METRO REGION: SOWHAT?

THE1 INLOVV WITH THENEW: TUFF QUESTN. HOW CANIGET ALLA ALICES SOCCR TEEEM INSIDE MYYY WEECAR? OURRR MJRLEAG HOTSHOT DZINE UNIT ASKED, WUTIF WEGO MODULAR? EXXTRA PASNGER SPACE WILLL SNAPONN! VOILA! ANND IDIDNOT WRINKLE MYTIE!

LA, OR MISS CNITALL B4: HEYBUDD! IDONT NEED BETTER CARSOK? INEED 2BFREE FROM THECAR. PERIOD.

KKARR VISNARY: YOUU HAV CHANGED ITHINK. *(ANOTHER PROMISE)* SMTHNLS IS DFN8LY DFFRNT. NOSTOPN 4GAS! MYNUKAR RUNSSSS ONA YET2BE DTRMND KLEEEN B9 SUBSTNC!

BIGCITY HADENUF: IMOVRYU. GETIT? IDONT1A LIVE LIKE THISS. SMOGYLA. POORKID STUCK NTRAFIK, SUFFRNG. ALONE NMYCAR. PAVED. FEDUP. YOUDO SUFK8ME. GETLOZT.

FUTURA MAN *(HEIS LIKE DAA DOPEMAN)*: UCANT GO 1STEP WITHOUT MEEEEE. IVEGOTU. GETTE USED2IT. ANYWAY, BEGR8FL 4MI TENDNCY

TO IMPROVE. *(BACK2 THERAP)* LITEW8 PLASTIX MOLDED N2 SENSUUS SLEEEK OVOID—

THECITY UPNARMS: DIDNTI TEL U2 LEAV? *(NRAGED, SHEGOES FORR HIS PHACE, WHICH DUZ FALLOFF REVEALN DUH MEMORY CHIPZ OFA ROBOT!)* UARE ATHING!

THETHNG: YIPES! NOFAIR! GIMME BACK MYFACE!

SNDIEGO 2SANTA BARBARA: YOUARE ATHINGY!

IT *(1MORE TRY)*: PUSHBTN WINDOZE! ELEVATD RODES! AIRBAGS! FORE BOTH SYDZ! IMEENIT!

CURTN

DAILY THOTS FER PEEPLE WHOOO DRIVIN ELLAYE

JAN1: FREEWAY UUTOPIA

IDREAM IAMM DRIVING ONDA FREEWAY 2HEAVN. TRAFICK DUZZ ZIPZIP ALONG. ALL LANES ARE OPEN. NOCARES.

WTARIDE! NOSMOG. NOQUAKE. NONO MUDSLYD. NO MULTI VEHICLE WREX. NOTONE OLDKAR DAT DUZZ STALL ND OFFRAMP ANNDD BLOCKIT ALLDAY. IDIDNOT SEE1 IMMATUR ANNOYNG TAILG8R WITH AN OBVIOUS HORMONL PROBLEM.

HAPPYME, IFEEL EL8ED. ITHINK, "ILIKEIT HERE." BE4 EVEN TURNING ONTHE RAYDIO IAM HEARING B80VEN9. IREAD THEPL8 ONDA KAR AHEAD. IT SEZ: URNICE.

NO1 MADE ERRATIK MOVES WHEN USINGA KARFONE. NOBODI KRASHS WILE PUTTN ON MASCARA AT 75MPH. EVRY1 YIELDED 2D OTHRGUY WITH AA POLITE WAVE. THEY SAY, "UGO1ST. PLEEESE." AND, "AFTRYOU, IMIN NOHURRY."

YEARITE.

TODAY IMGONNA GTAGRIP ONN REALITI.

JAN2: VALETPK

ZE LASTIME I8 ATA CHIC RSTRANT, ICAN NOT SAY IHADFUN. IAMMM
ONLEE HALF THERE. WHEN THE W8RDUDE TOOK DUH ORDER IHAD2
ASKHIM 2REPETE DAT SOUPE DUJOUR 3TIMES. SOMEHOW IDID END UPP
WITH APLATE UV SQUIDDD. REVOLTN. ALZO IKEEPON DROPIN MYY
SPOON.

ALLL ICOULD THINKK ABOUT WUZ THISSS: THAT VALETPK GUY LOOKD
CURRUPT. OR HUNGOVR.

ETHER WAAY IKNEW HEHAZ 2B GOINN THROUGH MI GLOV BOXXX ANNDD
CRANKNN UP ZEEE CD MACHINE AND MAKING OWT ONDA BAKSEAT.

HOWCANI LET DAT LOWKLAS JUVINAL DLNQUNT DRRRIVE OFF IN MYYY
IRPLCBL RIDE! AY CHIWAWA! IMNUTTZ!

TODAY IMGONNA REMEMBR SUMTHIN: ILVNLA. IPH IWANT2 NJOY
AMEAL ITZOK FORRE STRNGRZ TO TOUCH MEINKAR. (GULP!)

JAN3: BADDRVR

NOT LONGAGO IDID MEET AA FELLOW WHOSEZZ ZEEMOST PCULIAR
THINGG: "DONTELL 1SOUL, BUT IH82DRV."

ANDTHEN HESED, "SUMTIMZ ITHINK THAT MAYBEEE YN MYY NEXXXT
LIFE IWILLL FIGGA OWT HOWTO MERGE N2 ZE FREEWAY. IVNOW, IDO
THISSS: CLOSE MYIII AND HOPE4 ZEEBSST. BMBZAWY!

"PLUS ICANTC 2GOOD," HE WENTON. "ALZO IMDRIVN AKAR DAT HAZ
NOBRAIX."

ANOTHER TTIME II HEARD AAAA REKLESS RDMENIS SAY HOWCUM HEE
DUZZZ LIKE2 MAKE IMPE2US NUTHEAD LANE CHANGEZ:

"IOBJEKT TO THE CN4MITY ASPECT UV DRIVING," HEE SED. "STR8 LINES! PHOOIE! WHENNNN UCME CHANGE LANES USEEE ANARTST ATWORK. IAMAZEU. ISHOCKU. IGETU2C WHOUARE DEEPDWN."

2DAY ISHALL THINK ABOUT THIS: IN CAL4NIA EVEN AAAA GERBILL GETZ AAA LICENZ. SO IWILBE REALEEE REALI REALLLY CAREFUL.

JAN4: BADVIBE

MYFAULT. IWILLL NOT DENYIT. IDIDNT MEAN2 CUTOFF ZE WEIRDO ND
LL8 MODEL 4D, BUTYEAH IDID.

SO ZDUDE DUZ GIMMEE THA FINGER. HOEHUM. DAT DZNTMTR. BUT
ITHINK THE NRAGED CITIZEN ACT GOEZ ABIT OVRDTOP WHEN HEE
STARTS TU BANG HIZZ HEAD ONDA REARVU MIRROR.

ITZ ASIF AA TIMEBOM WENTOFF. ICANC HIM GETNALL WORKDUP,
LUZNIT RIGHT THERE ON ZE SANTAA MONIKA FREEWAY. IWATCH THEGUY
SKREEMN DRIVERS CURSES AT MEEEE. HE GOES:

"HAIBOZO YUSMELL. URTOAST YABUMYA. U8NOTHN UWORM, UAIRHED, UGOON. IMGONNA DSTROYU. YOU YESYOU. ILLRAMU, ILSUEU, ILLOWNU. BITETHS FATHEDD. EATDUST. BLABLAH BLA."

ON THISS DDAY IKAN CHOOZ 2PUT ONTHE TURN SIGNAL B4 AAAA VLNRABL UNSTABL DRIVER DUZ GOMAD.

MONDO
PL8SPK

DARWYNS THEORY UV EVOLUTN

IAMM SLIME. IMABUGG. IMSNAIL. IMSNAKE. IAMFISH. IMFROGY. IMARAT. AWEASEL. AA PORQPYN. IMELK. IMABIG YMARNR. IMATIGR, THAT MGNFSNT PRED8OR. IMABEAR. IAMA LEMUR. IM AMONKEE INATREE.

IMA BABOON. IAMMMM ACHIMP. IAM AN AWSOM LNGHAIR MOUNTIN GORILLA.

IAMMM CROMAGN MAN WEARN PELTZ, PAINTNG ONDA WAL OFA CAVEINN FRANCE. IMGEO AND IRAA GERSHWN HALINGA TAXICAB ON 7THAV. IMNOBDY LOOOKN N2 AMIRROR, FLOSSIN.

GR8 MOMENTS
IN AMERICN HIZTORY

YN 1988 THE GOP CANDID8 4US VEEPEA, DAN QUAYLE, DUZZ FACE
HIZZ DMOCRAT RIVAL, LLOYD BENTSON INNNN DB8. MANY MILYONS
WILLBEE SITTIN SPELBND B4 THER TEEVEEZ WHEN QUAILS YOUTH DUZ
BECOME ZEE BIGG QESTION.

SENATER DANQ: IM2 OLDNUFF 4DA JOB. JFK WUZ YOUNGR THANI AM
NOW WHENNN HEEE WENTE N2 OFFICE. SOTHERE!

SENATR LLOYDB: SENATYR, IKNEW JACK KENEDY. JAQ KENNEDY WAZ AFRIEND UV MYNE. ANNDD SENATUR, YOUARE NO JJACK KENNEDI.

SENATRR DANNNNY: OSHUTUP.

THAT ENDZ AA GREAT MOMENT INN AMURIKN HISTORI. YOUUU WILLL NOW BEEE RETURND TO UR REGULAR SCHEDUL PL8SPK.

ZE GR8GTSB

MOOLA: RICHH RRRRICH RIICH JGATSBY, THE SLFMADE RICHCAT, NEEEDED 2MAKMNY ANNDD MORMONY ANDMORE 2WINN BBACK DAYZEE, DONLY1 HEE DYD EVERLUV.

MEMOREE: 5YEARS B4 THEY HAD AN UN4GTBL AFFAIRE, ASWEET1. SHE SEEMD TTO SAY, "UATLAST! IMURLVR JAY 4KEEPS." ODAISY. BYNDHIP, YNGNRCH, ALWAYZ RDY4FUN, GORJUS AND IRI6TBL. GATSB WANTZII HAV LLLOVE FROZEN NTIME.

ME: IAMNICK CARAWAY, THA NAR8R. HERES DREASNI KNO SOMUCH: FOLKS WILLLLL TELME NETHNG. PLUS ILIVE NEXTT DOOR2 GATSBEE.

THATZ HIMCELF GOING, "HELLLOO OLSPORT." ANDIAM 2ND COUSYN 2DAISY.

MARRIED: INNN 1918 JJAYG GOEZ OFF 2D WAR. SHEEZ IMP8NT. WEDS AGOON WITH POLO PONIES, AROGANT TOMM BUKANAN. OLDMONY. NOW THAYRE LIVNON SNOOOTY LNGILND. BASIQLY THEEZE TWO ARE ALIKE: SLFCTRD, MEE1ST, IMEMINE.

MMERRY MAKING: THATT1 SUMMR, 2MANYA REVELER SERUSLY IN2LIQR MECCA EQUALS GATSBYS. HEIZ GIVIN OUTR8JS PARTEES, HOPING DAISY MITE DROPIN. ALLL LNGISLN PLUS NOOYORK GOEZ FRANTYK THERE, BOOZIN TILDAWN. (EVRY1 LETS CHRLSTN!) SUMDAYS IWOULD FIND MMMANYA POSH GUEST OUTCOLD ON MYYY STEPS. AS4 DAIZEY, NOLUCK. SO MII NAYBOR WIL ASKMEE 2DO SUMTHNG TU HELP.

MOONLHT: ATNITE, GATZBEE DUZZ STANNDE ONN HIS BEACH INNNN WEST EGGG LOOKING N2 DARKNIS. WILE WATCHIN AA BLINKIN LITE FRRROMM DAYSIZ DOCK YN EAST EGG, HEEE KANTSEE THAT HEES BETROFF HAVING AFANTAZ THANN TRYNG2 RECRE8 ATIME B4DWAR.

MAKNLUV: ANDTHEN,THNX2ME, HENSHE MEET NZFLESH. 1DERRRR DUZZ NEARLEE OVRWELM GGATSBY. ALLHIS CRE8V PASSHUN WENTE N2DREMN THISSS. SHEGOZ, "YESIDO ABSLTLI LUVYU." ANND ANYWAE TTTTOM DUZ VISIT AAAA MISTRSS, SSSSHE ISS ALMOST CERTAIN. GATZBE DUZZZ NTISIP8 THERR PHINE XILR8IN FUTURE 2GETHER.

MELTING: HOTTEST DDAY OFD SUMMMR, CZLNHOT. LUNCH AT DAISEYS NNN TOMMZZ. IMTHERE. ALSO DAISIES FREND JJORDON, THELADY GOLFPRO. ANNDE GATTSB. DRINKX 4ALL. THOM DDUS H8 GATSBIE.

TENSION GROWS. "LETSS GO2TOWN. IWANT2 HAVPHUN," DAYZ SEZ. "FNFNFUN." TOMMMM SAYSSS, "WHISKEY. IGOTITT."

MANHATN: WEGO N2CARZ. FORR NOGOOD REASON WEEEE TAKE AAA ROOM INTHE PLAZA HOTEL. DAISYY IZ VERRRY, "OOOOH THISSS HEETWAV!" GATSBY NNNN HIZ RIVAL STRUGGL 2THNAIL ABOUT WHOOOO GETZ2 KEEP DAYZEE. "UR AN OUTNOUT FRAUD," SEZ1. "DSAME2U," SAYSSS DUH OTHER1.

MNDGAMZ: GATSBI NEEDS DAISIE TO TELUS SSSSHE NEVER LUVVED HERR SPOUSE. "UWANTII MUCH," SHEGOZ, UPSET, QUNFUZD. "II DIDDID LUVHIM, ANDU2." "ULUVME2?" HESED BAK. "WHAAAAT? ULOVEME TOO?" NCRDABL! THIS SPEECH UV HERS HAS2 DESTROI GATSBYS BRAYN. TOM GOES, "HEHEHEH, ULUZPAL."

MOTORIN: DAYZY DECIDES 2DRIVE JAYSCAR BACKHOM. ANDFAST. ONDAWAY SHEEEEE RUNSSSS DOWNN ALADY IN DA ROAD. DEAD. HITNRUN. IDUNNO IF DAISEE EVR HERDDAT SHE HITT TOMS GRLFRND, MRS WILSON.

MAYHEM: DUH KRAZED HUBBO WILLLLL CRAVE RAVENGE. "HEYYBUD YOUDO NOTT WANTME," TOMTOM SAID TOHIM. "MRGATZB IZZZZ ZE KILLER. HEZ THE1 WHO NVRSTPS, LEAVING URHONEY ONDROAD LIKE SUM DOGGY." SO WILSN SHOOTS GATZBY BANG DED ANDTHEN WALKS AWAAAY, DAA KORPS BOBBIN UPNDWN INTHE POOL.

MONEY: SOOON DAZEY ANND TOMMO SPLIT LONGISL. OTHER DAMM PEOPLE CAN CLEANUP THEMESS. OBLVIUS, ABVITAL, DEY ALWAYSS RETREET BAK N2 THERRR MONIE. ATLEEST PASHN8 YESSS VULGAR GATTSB CANN DREEEM.

MORE: TOHIM, AS ITDOES TTO ALOTTA AMRICAN FOLKS, LYFE PROMISZ 2B U4RIK 1DAY. LOOK AT THEM KRASH N2DFUTR, THINKN IMCLOSE, ICAN TOUCH IT. BUT WEARE LYKE BOATS BORNNE BYYYY ZEE CURRENT, CARRIED ENDLSLY BACK N2 THEPAST.

SILENT SPRINGE

ITHAPNZ INA TOWN, MAYBEE SOMTING LYKE URTOWN. LIFE DUZ
KARRYON 1SEASON FOLLOIN ANOTHER. HAPPI SUMMRS CUMNGO. AUTUMN
DAZZLES, ITDOES AMAZE. WNTRTYM, LITTL CRITTRS KNOWHOW TO FIND
BERRIES INSNOW.

   SPRINGE. LONBHLD THIS SPELL, ANEVIL1, DUZZ TAKEOVR. WEREVIR
FOLKS LOOK AROUND: DEDDUX, DDED CHIXX, NOCOWS YN ZAT MEADOW
OUTHER, SHEEP GETSICK ANDIE. AA STRANGE BLIGHT CHANGEZ
EVRYTNG.

WEIRDED OWT MDS SEE PATIENS GOUNDAR INA2ND. XUBRANT KIDDOZ GGONE LIKEDAT. THEDOCS SED, "UMM, DONTASK MMME. II CNTXPLN IT."

ITSO QUIETT, INONE NOTKOOL SORTOF WAY. THBIRDS, 4EXAMPL. WHAHAPN 2EM? NONE ARRIVE AT BAKYARD FEEDERS. DIS SPRNG HAZ NNNOE VOICES. AMS B4 DYD THROB WYTHE THA DAWNNNN CHORUS: ROBINZZ, JJAYZ, DOVES, WRENS ETALIA DDID 4MERLY SINGOUT. THSTIME NADA. SILENCE, DATSALL.

WITCHS DIDIT ORR 4N AGENTS ORELSE PERVRSE ALIEN BEINGS. UTHNKSO? NOPE. ZEE FOOLISH PEEPLE MADE THEIR OWN AGONEE.

AFTER WWII AMERIKA WENTMAD 4AAA NEWTOY: KLORN8D HYDRO CARBON INSECT KILLER POISONZ. SUDDNLY ALLOVER THEUS THE HIEST VALUE CAME2 BE THIS1: DEDBUGS.

NOTHNG MUST GET NTHEWAY OFD PERSONN WITH DA SPRYGUN. IPH
PETS DROPDED AND RAKOONZ, BARNYRD ANIMLZ, LARKS, POSSUMM,
PHEASNT PLUS SALMON DO2, THENN TUFF. WEDID TURN OUR F8
OVER2EZ 2SOME GUYZ ONA DETHTRP WHOO KEEPON SPEAKIN 2WORDS:
SPRAY MORE.

MEANTYM MANYA CHEMICL DEALER GOES, "HUCARES! WERRICH!" WAR
ONTHE FIREANT BRINGS DEVST8N 2TEXAS, LUZIANA, ALABAMA,
GEORGIA, ANNDE FLORIDA. ONE ALLOUT REKLISS CAMPAIN TTO ELIMN8
JAPNEEZ BEETLES SHATERD ECOLOGI INTHE MIDWST. NN DETROIT,
POWDER LIKE DDT ONLY ALOT WORSE FELL INNA DREDFUL BLZZZRD.

BYYYY SEEKING 2CONQUR JUSTA HANDFUL OF UNWANTD SPECIES,
INTLGNT PEOPLE DDID ALLOW POYZYN 2B SPREAD EVRYWHR ONEARTH.

H2O, SOIL, PLANTZ, AMEBAS, ZE REMOTE ARCTIK PLRBAER: ALLOFEM
TAINTD. EVEN THEMOST LLITTLE NEON8 CHILDE HAS CHMICLS INSYDE.

AAAAA DEDLY TOXXIC RAIN FALLS DOWN NONSTOP. ALLTHAT KILLN.
4WHAT? UPNCOMN INSECTE STRAINS LAFF OFF WWHATT USED2B LETHL.
DUSTEM 2DMX 1SUMMER; NXTYEAR, THERBAK.

SUPREAM COURT MEMBER WILLYUM OH DOUGLAS WROTEIT: 4A SOCIETI
2BJUST, WEHAV2 SUPPORT HUMNRTS, NOTT 4GETN OURRRR RITE2
ANATRL NVRNMNT.

ENUFFF AROGANT THINKN. ENUFF BEHAVIN CAVEMAN STYYLE. IF
WEDONT GETOVER THISS FIX8TED NEED 2CONTRL NATURE, SMDAY SOON
RPLANET WILLL BEDEAD.

MAEWEST GOEZ OUT2EAT

OHW8ER, ISDAT AGUNN YN UR POCKETT OR AREYOU JUST GLADD
2SEEMEE? HOWZA LNGUINI?

THEBOOK OF JOB

1DAY GODD ANND SATAN WER TALKING. GODSAID, "WHERE HAVEYOU BIN LATELEE?" SAYTON ANSWRED, "ONEARTH, WALKNG 2ANFRO."

SAID THELORD, "SO YOUMUST KNO MYMAN JOB. HEEE DOTH FEARGOD ANNDD ALWAZE TURNZ AWAAAAY FROM EEEVIL. NONE IZZ LYKE HIM ANYWHRE ONN EARTH."

THDEVIL DYD REPLY, "QUEL SRPRIZE! UGOT SSOM COMFY RICHCAT GOIN HALLUYA. IBETCHA HEWILL CURSEU TO UR FAACE IPH YOUUU EVER START2 MESSS WITH HIZ GOODIES."

DLORD SEZ, "BEHOLD, IGIVE2U ZPOWER 2CONTRL ALLL DAT HEHAZ. JUST DONT GIVEM ANY FIZIKAL PAINE. NOW SCRAMM." ANNDD DPRINCE OFD DARKNSS DDID GOAWAYY FROMGOD.

THENN QUIKLEE JOBE LOSTALL. OXEN, SHEEP, CAMELLS: GONE. 4N RAEDERZ CAME2 STEAL THEMM ANDTHEN DIDDID SLAY MMMANYA SERVANT. FIRE DUZ CONSUME MMMMORR. ATLASTA GR8 WIND DOES DESTROY HIZZ OLDEST KIDZ HOUSE. ALLL HISSS CHILDRN DIE. 7SONS AND 3DAWTRS.

SO THISGUY SHAVES HIZZZZ HEADD ANDIS YN DEEEP MORNING. HESED, "NAKID II CAME FFFROMM MIMOMS WOOM, NAKED IWILGO. DELORD GAVE, ZLORD TOOK AWAAAY. BLESDBE HISNAME."

GODSEZ TU SAYTIN, "II TOLDUSO. ZDUDE 8NTBAD." ZDEVIL GOES,

"BUTGOD, HEIS STL HELTHY. GIVEM HORRBLE SKINN CRUDD ANDIAM CERTAIN HEES GONNA CURSYOU TOYER FACE."

SOON JOBS BODY WILLBE ONE GRUESOM SSOR. OAGONY, HED2TOE. HE SITTS INTHE ASHES USINGA BROKEN BIT OF POTTERY TTO SKRATCH HMSELF. YET WRETCHD AS THEMAN HATH BECOMME, NO1 EVER KAN HEARHIM SPEAKIN THISWAY: "IH8U OLAWD."

HISWIFE GOEZ, "ITHINK URS2PID MAN! BETTER2 DAMM GOD AND DIEBABY!" JOBBO SAYS, "GUDNBAD, IACCEPT GODSWIL."

4SEVEN DAYS HEZ SITTIN NDADIRT, MUTE, SUFFRNG. MEENTYM 3PALS ARRIVE. "WEWILL CCOMFRT RFRIEND," THEY SAY.

ANDNOW JJOB, BITTER, SILENT NOMORE, STARTS RAGINON ABOUT HISLIFE ANDE F8.

"YMEGOD?'' SAYS THISS SORRY HMNBEAN. "IZZZZ DIS WTIDSRV?"

"LKATTHS FLESH. IMROTN. KIDDS CRY, 'OHGROSS!' MIWIFE, SHEDUZ ADVIZ MEEEE ITZ TYM2DIE. IMBKRPT, MORBID, NFECTED, LIVING IN UNBRABL TORMENT, UNLOVED, DWNNOUT, SIKOLIF. ITHURTS."

AFRIEND SEZ, "OHMERCY. PLEEZDO NOT GIMME DAT INNOCNT VICTIM MUMBO JUMBOH."

"BUT IAM1, PAL," JOBY GOSE. "DONTU BLAMEME. IMNOT AFELON. 2DAY FOLKS SPITTT ONME. YET, B4, IUSE2 GIVEM PHOOOD, MONEE, SOMWEAR 2REST."

ANOTHER DUBIOUS BUDDEE SED, "INOGOD MYFREN. ANDI KNOW AAAA DSPKABL CINPHUL BASSTUD WHENNNN ISEE1. FACEIT. YELSE HAS RLAWD PUNISHD USOBAD?"

"BEKAUZ THERIS NO JUSTICE!" SAYSS DA UN4CHN8 WRETCH.

4DAYS THEEZE GUYSS ARE ARGUIN BCKN4TH. OVRNOVR JOBER WILLGO ON2 ASSERT HISSS NTGRTY. HESED OUTLOUD, "MILORD, DEARGOD, YCANTU COME2ME ANDSO TELLME MIII CRIME?"

THENA WRLWIND KAME DWN2RTH. ITTIZZ THE ALMGHTY HIMCELF.

HESED, "STANDUP LITLMAN. IAMMMM TALKN2U. WHRWERU WHEN IMADE EVRYTHN? EVRYTNG! CANYUU CRE8 ICE? NO? HOWBOUT BIRTH ITSELF? NOOO? MADE ANY HIPPOS LATELEE, BIGSHOT?"

JOBO SSEZ, "OKUWIN, IGIVVUP. URRIGHT, WTDOINO? THY WAYZ RR NDSI4BL 2MEEEE."

INDA END THEPOOR SOUL RECOVRD. TTHE CRE8OR RETURND ALLDAT HEE LOST, NTHNSUM. HELIVZ ALONG LYFE. HAZ LOTSOF NEWKIDS, TOO.

KNGLEAR

GGO HAV KKIDS.

DICKENZ AA XMAS KAROLLE

1AND ALLLOVE CHRSTMS. NEWAYZ DATZ WHATT UTHINK.

"BAHH! HUMBUGG!"

MEETT EB SKROOGE. HE SEZ, "DEC25TH. IH8IT. BAAH!"

ITSEEMZ NOTHN KAN LUSENUP THIS NFAMOUS BITTER NOGOOD NNASSTY OLCREEP. SSOM XMPLS FOLLO.

MRMEAN TALKS ABOUT HOLIDAAE GDHUMOR: "LETS TORTURE FOOLS WHO GOROUND AND BABBLE MRIXMAS. BOYLE EM, ISAY, XMAS PUDDING STYYLE."

ONN CHARITY: "CURSES! HOMELES PEEPL! DONTBSO PHAST SPENDIN MYMONEY. HUMBUG! LET THEM DI. IDNTCRE."

ON GIVING 1DAYOFF 2BOB, HIZ LOYAL CLERK, 2B WITH DA WIFE, KDSNDOG 4NOEL: "UDOIT 2ME EVREY 25DEC, FIEND. OALLRT. STAY ATHOME 2MORO. GEESH!"

THAT NITE SCROOGE HASA FULBLWN XSTNSHL CRISIS. 1BY1 AA GHOZT TRIO DUZZ VISIT HIZ BED.

"LTSGO WAYBAC 2A XMASPST," SAYSS GHOST1. "IWANNA SHOWYOU SUMTHNG NTRSTNG."

"HLYSMOK," GOEZ DOLDMAN. "II USED2 BACHILD ONCE. I4GOT."

NVZABLE LYKDWND GHOST2 DUZ FLYEM STR8 TU CHEZBOB, THEHOME UV EBS LLONG SUFFRNG WORKER. THE2 SEEBOB ARRIVE NND HISSON

TINYTIM RIDING BOBSS BACK. MESSDUP WYTHE AAA MUSCLE DISEASE, HEHAZ TO.

W8N INSYDE THERZ THFMILY. KULMOM ANNDD NOTONE ROTNKID AMONGM. ENTER BOBNSON 2CHEERS: "YIPPEE POPPO! WELUVU! WELUV OURLIL LAMEGUY TIMMIE TOO! WR2GTHR ANDD THISIS ENUF4US. XMASJOY JOYOJOY!"

"ATOSTE," BOBSAYS. "MRRYXMS MYDEARS. GODBLSS THISS CLANNE."

"GDBLSUS EVRY1," ECHOZ TNY TIM. THISISA BLISSFL SCENE EVEN NUTZO OURHERO CANDIG.

2DOWN 1TOGO. GHOST3 SHOWSE EBNZER CHRSMAS FUTURE. (BWARE. DIS NEXXT PART 8NT4KDS.)

SCROOGE DEAD. FOLKS SAY: "ATLAST." TINIE TIMTIM DEAD2.

FRAGYL 2XS, HEFEL AVICTIM OF HIDEOUS POVERTY. HISDAD DOES
FEEL THEPAIN IMENSLY.

"IGETIT! IREPENT!" EBNEEZR CRYS. "WUTEVER ISED B4 RE
THEPOOR ANDALSO THEWEAK: ERASE ZE TAPE. SUDNLY, BLAMMO,
INOBETR. THATKID MUSTBE SAVED!"

SAYHI TTTOO THENEW SCROOGY. NEXTDAY, XMASDAY, THEDUDE
SENDSS BOBBO ETAL AMONSTR TURKEY.

MAKING OUT ONE WAYBIG CHECK 4DA NEEDY, EBBY GOES, "NDEEED
ILVXMAS."

BOBWILL GET1 HEFTY RAISE. TEETEE DIDNOT DIYUNG. EBNEZER
WILLB LIKA 2ND POPPA TOHIM ANNDE AGUDGUY 2ONE NN ALLL.

ODE 2BILLI JJOE
(SPECHUL NEWW FFRENCH VERZIN)

IBEEN CUTTINN DDOWN COTTN ALLL MORNINN. OUIOUI. DAT WOULDBE
ONN JUNE3RD. AA SLEEPI DDUSTY DELTAA DDAYE. HOTHOTT HHOTT.
IMTELLN YAAAA, 2DANG CHAUDE.

   BBACK2 LESHACK 4LUNCH. MAMAN SHEIS ABOUT2 PASS2ME SOME
FROMAGE WHENNNN SHEGOZ, "IGOT NEWS 2DAY FRRROMM CHOKTAW RIDGE.
BILYJO MCALSTR DDID JUMPOFF LE BRIDGE UPTHERE. IL EST MORT."

IWANT2 CRI, "MAISNON! YALL MAKINIT UPP." HOWEVR IMUST KEEP STILL. IVE GOTTA SECRET.

MONPERE HESED, "ALORS, ZISSSSS BEELY JOH NEVER HADA LICK OF SENS ANYHOWW. DONNEY MOI LEPAIN ANDMORE BEURRE, WOODYA?"

2PAPA BBBILLY JOZE FATAL LEAP MATTERS LESSS THANN LA BAGETTE.

MON FRER HESED, "OOHLALA! DIDNTI SEEYAA TALKNG TOHIM AFTER ZEE CHURCH LAST SUNDAYE? ANOTHER PIECE UV PIE POURMOI, OKAAY?"

I1TTOO REPLY, "OBROTHR, STOP TALKNG ABOUTME, SIL VOUS PLAY."

MAMERE SHEDUZ GO, "ZAT NICE YUNG PREACHR BROTHAA TAYLOR SAID ZATYOU AND BILLIJO WAZ SEEN THROWEN QUELQUE CHOSE OFF THA BRIDGE."

IAMM LIKE, "MONDIEU! SSSSHE KNOWS!" BUT SHE NEVEUR SED NOTHN BOUT BILLIE JOE AFTER ZATT1 DAI. RIEN. NEITHER DIDI. HOW BIZARRR.

SOON MYY PHAMILY WOULDE KINDA JUST FADAWAY. BROTHER WED BEKKI THOMSON ANNDD 2DSWEET THAY OPENED LAA BOUTEEK IN TUPELO. LAST SPRINGE WE DYD BURRY PPAPA ANDNOW PETITE CHERE MAMAA SHEEEEE IZZ TRES UNHAPPY.

ME, IGO UPP2 CHOCTAW RDGE TOUT LETEMPS 2PIKKE LES FLEURS ANDTHEN DROPMM OFF LLE PONT.

GLOSSARY

A

ABSLTLI absolutely
ABVITAL above it all
AHEDOVU ahead of you
AL1 alone
AU2MATQ automatic

B

BAGRESV be aggressive
BEURRE *beurre* [Fr.] butter
BGOTT1 begotten
BGRNLFE bigger than life
BYNDHIP beyond hip
BYRLST8 buy real estate

C

CHAUDE *chaude* [Fr.] hot
CHERE *chere* [Fr.] dear
CLDBLDD cold-blooded
CMPTRZD computerized
CNITALL seen it all
CNTMPL8 contemplate
COGITO *cogito* [Lat.] I think
CRFTMN craftsman
CROMAGN Cro-Magnon

D

DFN8LY definitely
DHRDWY the hard way
DLWITIT deal with it

DONNEY MOI *donnez moi* [Fr.] give me
DREASNI the reason I
DSNTMTR doesn't matter
DVST8N devastation
DZNTMTR doesn't matter

E

EMSHNL emotional
EVEN2LY eventually

F

F8LEE fatally
FIGGA figure
FLTBSH Flatbush
FRER *frère* [Fr.] brother
FROMAGE *fromage* [Fr.] cheese

G

GETNALL getting all

H

HALINGA hailing a
HENSHE he and she

I

ICANC I can see
ICANTC I can't see
IDNTCRE I don't care
IDONT1A I don't wanna
IH82DRV I hate to drive
IL EST MORT *il est mort* [Fr.] he is
  dead
IMAJIN imagine

IMP8NT impatient
IMPE2US impetuous
IMUPALD I'm appalled
IMURLVR I'm your lover
INNOSNT innocent
INNOV8V innovative
I1TTOO I want to
IRI6TBL irresistible
IRPLCBL irreplaceable
IVNOW for now

K

KDSNDOG kids and dog
KLORN8D chlorinated

L

LAA BOUTEEK *la boutique* [Fr.] the store

LA BAGETTE *la baguette* [Fr.] loaf of French bread
LEPAIN *le pain* [Fr.] the bread
LFSABMR life's a bummer
LGNABCH Laguna Beach
LLE PONT *le pont* [Fr.] the bridge
LNGILND Long Island
LONBHLD lo and behold
LOOK4WD look forward
LVT2BVR Leave It to Beaver

M

MAISNON *mais non* [Fr.] but no
MAKMYDY make my day
MAKNZS making z's
MAMAN *maman* [Fr.] mama
MAMERE *ma mère* [Fr.] my mother

MBRACME embrace me
MHPYNOW I'm happy now
MHVNFUN I'm having fun
MONDIEU *mon dieu* [Fr.] my God
MONPERE *mon père* [Fr.] my father
MYIII my eyes

N

NADA *nada* [Sp.] nothing
NAR8R narrator
ND in the
NDSI4BL indecipherable
NEMOORE anymore
NETHING anything
NEWAYZ anyways
NOWORYZ no worries
NTHNSUM and then some

NTISIP8 anticipate
NVRSTPS never stops
NYAKTOR New York actor

P

POURMOI *pour moi* [Fr.] for me
PRESHS1 precious one

Q

QUEL *quel* [Fr.] what
QUELQUE CHOSE *quelque chose* [Fr.]
  something

R

RDMENIS road menace
RGOSUM *ergo sum* [Lat.] therefore I am
RIEN *rien* [Fr.] nothing

RKHAVOC wreak havoc
RN4YRLF run for your life

S

SCRNRTR screenwriter
SIKOLIF sick of life
SIL VOUS PLAY *s'il vous plaît* [Fr.]
   please
SMTHNLS something else
SONAV son of

T

THOZII those two
THOZIII those eyes
TOUT LETEMPS *tous les temps* [Fr.] all
   the time

U

U8NOTHN you ain't nothin'
U4RIK euphoric
UN4CHN8 unfortunate
UWANTII you want too

V

VALETPK valet parking
VERZIN version
VLNRABL vulnerable
VRYSCRY very scary

W

WANTZII wants to
WR2GTHER we're together
WTIDSRV what I deserve

X

XKWIS8 exquisite
XSTNSHL existential

Y

YIAWTTA why, I oughtta
YMARNR weimaraner
YMINLA why am I in LA

1DERRRR wonder
1STKLSS first class
2DMX to the max
2DSWEET *tout de suite* [Fr.] quickly
2PANGA Topanga
2THNAIL tooth and nail
2TSIE tootsie
2XS to excess
3LLLING thrilling
4D Ford
4MERLY formerly
8NTEZ ain't easy
8NT4KDS ain't for kids